## *WHAT IT MEANS TO BE*
## SERIES

| | |
|---|---|
| PUBLISHER | Joseph R. DeVarennes |
| PUBLICATION DIRECTOR | Kenneth H. Pearson |
| ADVISORS | Roger Aubin |
| | Robert Furlonger |
| EDITORIAL MANAGER | Jocelyn Smyth |
| EDITORS | Ann Martin |
| | Shelley McGuinness |
| | Robin Rivers |
| | Mayta Tannenbaum |
| ARTISTS | Richard Comely |
| | Greg Elliott |
| | Summer Morse |
| | Barbara Pileggi |
| | Steve Pileggi |
| | Mike Stearns |
| PRODUCTION MANAGER | Ernest Homewood |
| PRODUCTION ASSISTANTS | Catherine Gordon |
| | Kathy Kishimoto |
| PUBLICATION ADMINISTRATOR | Anna Good |

**Canadian Cataloguing in Publication Data**

Prasad, Nancy
  What it means to be—honest

(What it means to be; 25)
ISBN 0-7172-2282-9

1. Honesty — Juvenile literature.
I. Pileggi, Steve.    II. Title.    III. Title: Honest.    IV. Series.

BJ1533.H7P73 1987    j179'.9    C87-095068-1

# WHAT IT MEANS TO BE...

## HONEST

Written by
**Nancy Prasad**

Illustrated by
**Greg Elliott**

**Being honest means telling the truth.**

Mom had been baking cookies for her bridge party that night. When Jason came home from school he could smell them. "Yum!" he said. They were double chocolate chip, his favorite kind. His mother had gone out and his father was talking on the phone, so there was no one to ask whether he could have a cookie or not. He decided to try one. Then he had another and another . . . They were delicious.

When his mother returned home she noticed that a lot of cookies were missing from the plate.

"Oh, no!" she cried. "Who could have . . . ?"

"Me," said Jason, looking a little green. "And I wish I hadn't."

---

When you've done something wrong, it's best to admit it right away. Others will respect you for being honest and you'll be glad you told the truth.

**Honest people take responsibility for their mistakes.**

One day Tammy and Colette's father brought home a mysterious box. "You'll never guess what I've got in here," he said.

Colette read the top of the box. "Ice cream!" she cried. "What kind did you get, Dad?"

"Any kind you want," he said as he pulled out a shiny metal thing.

Tammy was disappointed. "That's not ice cream," she complained. "It's a machine."

"It's a machine that makes ice cream," their father explained. "What kind shall we make first?"

"Strawberry," both girls agreed.

The ice cream was wonderful. That night, when the rest of her family was watching TV, Tammy decided to try to make some all by herself.

She put in some banana yogurt and some peanuts. It didn't look the way it had when her father had made it, but she wasn't worried. She turned the crank a few times.

Bubble gum—that's what her ice cream needed.

Tammy chewed a few pieces of gum and then added it to the mixture. She turned the crank. Now it was ready for the freezer.

The next morning when Tammy went down for breakfast, Dad looked very cross.

"Colette, I told you not to play with the ice-cream machine," he said sternly.

"But, Dad—"

"I want you to clean it out right now," he stated. "And I hope you haven't broken the crank."

Tammy piped in, "It wasn't Colette, Dad. It was me. I was trying to make a new kind of ice cream."

"Oh," their father said. "I'm sorry I blamed you, Colette. Tammy, you know you're not supposed to use it unless I'm supervising you."

"I'm sorry. I'll clean it out," Tammy offered.

It took a while to unstick all the gum but soon the machine was as good as new. Tammy made sure from then on that she did exactly as her father told her whenever she helped to make ice cream.

---

Sometimes you may do something you know you shouldn't do. Always admit what you have done and try to make up for it.

**Be honest to yourself.**

Tammy was playing in the schoolyard before kindergarten when Hannah came running up to her. "Guess what?" cried Hannah. "My guppies had babies last night. They're so tiny. I'll take you to my house to see them."

"I can't wait," said Tammy. "I've never seen baby guppies before."

While they were playing ball, Tammy saw Colette. "Hannah's got something special to show me," Tammy told her. "Tell Mom and Dad I'll be at her house after school."

After school, Hannah was so busy talking with Janice that she walked halfway home before she remembered she had forgotten to take Tammy home with her.

Hannah wondered if she should go back to school. "I'm sure Tammy got tired of waiting," she said to herself. "She must have gone home with Colette or Mitchell."

Suddenly it started to rain so Hannah ran home as fast as she could.

A while later Hannah started to feel badly. What if Tammy hadn't gone home? She decided to call Tammy's house.

"She's not here," said Tammy's dad. "I thought she went to your house."

"I forgot to meet her," admitted Hannah.

"I'll pick you up and you can help me look for Tammy," he said.

They drove to school in the pouring rain. There was Tammy, waiting by the door of their classroom.

Hannah felt terrible. "Oh, Tammy," she said. "I'm so sorry that I forgot to meet you."

"You promised to show me your guppies," said Tammy. "You *promised!*"

---

Once in a while you may be tempted to lie to yourself, so that something you've done wrong—like breaking a promise—doesn't seem so bad. If you are honest, you will try to always tell the truth to yourself as well as to others.

**Honest people do not cheat.**

Each Friday, Ms. Barclay gave the first grade class a spelling test. Paul hated spelling. He was one of the poorest spellers in the class and had just about given up studying for the tests.

Then Paul thought of a way to get a perfect score. ''I'll show everybody,'' he thought as Ms. Barclay started reading out the words.

The easy words were first, but when they got harder, Paul slid a copybook out of his desk onto his lap and started copying the hard words.

When the tests were marked, Paul's paper was perfect.

Ms. Barclay said, ''You must have worked very hard, Paul. You spelled every word correctly.''

Paul's face turned very red. ''Ms. Barclay, I didn't study hard. I copied from my notebook.''

Ms. Barclay made him stay after school to write why he shouldn't cheat.

---

If you don't do your own work, you will end up cheating yourself because you won't learn what you need to know. Trying your hardest is what's really important.

**You can be honest without hurting people's feelings.**

Hannah's father was standing on a ladder, painting the house while Hannah and Mitchell played tag nearby. "Be careful," said her dad. "I want paint on the house, not on you."

"Don't worry," said Hannah. "We'll play on the other side of the house. That's out of the way."

But they soon got so caught up in their game that they forgot about Hannah's father painting. Mitchell was chasing Hannah. She ran faster and faster to get away from him—right around the house and into the ladder. Her father dropped his roller covered in paint right on Hannah's head.

"Ouch!" she yelped, rubbing her sore head. It felt wet and sticky. Her hair was covered with white paint.

"Oh, Hannah," cried Mitchell. "Poor you!"

Hannah's mother tried to get the paint out of Hannah's hair, but nothing seemed to work. "I'm afraid you're going to have to get it cut," she said.

Later that day, Dylan and Mitchell came to see how Hannah was. She didn't want to see them. When she finally came out of the house, she had a scarf tied around her head.

"Take off that silly scarf," said Mitchell. "We want to see your new haircut."

"I feel awful," moaned Hannah. "I don't look like me at all. See," she said as she took off the scarf.

Paul was riding by on his scooter. "What did you do to your hair? You look weird!"

Hannah looked as if she was going to cry, so Dylan quickly said, "I think your short hair is neat."

"You do look different," added Mitchell. "But the best thing about hair is that it grows quickly. Soon you'll look like your old self again."

---

People are very sensitive about how they look. It's best to be truthful in a kind way when you comment on your friend's appearance—or else say nothing at all.

**It is important to be honest about your feelings.**

"I love scary things," said Ryan as he sat with his friends in the tree house. "A new scary movie is coming to town—*Godzilla Meets the Swamp Monster.* Cameron is taking me to see it on Saturday and he said I could bring some friends."

"Great!" exclaimed Dylan. "I'd love to come."

"Me too," said Kim.

Joey didn't say anything.

"You'll come too, won't you, Joey?" asked Ryan.

"I don't know," said Joey. "I'll have to ask my parents."

That night, Joey told his parents about his friends' plan to see the movie. "Sure, you can go. If you want to," said Joey's mom.

"That's the problem," admitted Joey. "I want to be with my friends, but I don't like monster movies. They scare me too much."

"Just tell them how you feel," suggested his dad.

"I'm afraid they'll laugh at me," Joey said sadly.

The next day when Ryan met Joey he asked, "What did your parents say?"

Joey spoke in a low voice. "They said I could see the movie—if I want to."

Ryan chuckled. "Of course you want to."

On the way to the movie, the kids were laughing and making monster sounds—everyone except Joey.

"What's the matter, Joey?" asked Kim.

Joey looked at Kim's sympathetic face. "Oh, Kim," he burst out. "I love funny movies, but monster movies scare me. What am I going to do?"

"Why didn't you say so?" said Kim. "There's a funny movie playing in the same theater. We could see that one instead of *Godzilla Meets the Swamp Monster*. I like comedies too."

When it came time to buy their tickets, Kim said, "Joey and I are going to see the funny movie next door. We'll meet outside after the show."

"Thanks, Kim," whispered Joey.

---

Part of being honest is telling people how you really feel about things. Friends and family appreciate knowing your true feelings.

**Honest people do not make up stories to fool others.**

Lately Mitchell had been feeling left out. His mom and dad always seemed to be busy and didn't have much time for him. The older kids didn't like him hanging around. Even Tammy seemed to be playing with Janice and Hannah more than with him.

Mitchell tried to think of exciting things to tell people so they would pay more attention to him. The trouble was, there weren't that many exciting things in Mitchell's life. So he started making things up.

One day he saw Tammy and Janice playing in the sandbox. ''My dad's getting me a python for a pet,'' said Mitchell. ''It's so huge we'll have to keep it in the basement. It only eats live animals like mice and frogs. And it can squeeze a person to death!''

All afternoon Mitchell told them python stories. He felt happy watching their eyes grow wide with amazement.

"When can we see him?" asked Tammy.

"Soon," said Mitchell.

In a few days, Tammy and Janice went to call on Mitchell. "We came to see Mitchell's new pet," said Tammy.

"You must mean his snake," said Mitchell's mother. "It's in his room."

The girls looked scared. "I thought it was in the basement," said Tammy.

"Not this little fellow," laughed his mom, taking them over to a small glass cage. The girls looked inside.

"Why it's only a grass snake," exclaimed Tammy. "That Mitchell!" Tammy and Janice started laughing.

Then Mitchell told Dylan there was a ghost in his basement that groaned and moaned at night. "You can only see it in the dark," said Mitchell.

Dylan was excited. After dinner, he came with a flashlight to see Mitchell's ghost. But all he saw was the furnace and some stored boxes.

"Some ghost," sneered Dylan. "I must have been crazy to believe you."

Soon Mitchell was as lonely as before. He decided to visit Tammy.

"You promise you won't make up any stories?" she asked.

"But I thought you liked my stories," he answered.

"Not if you pretend they're true," she explained.

---

An honest person doesn't fool people by exaggerating or telling "tall tales" just to get attention. If people know you are honest, they will be interested in what you have to say.

**Help younger brothers and sisters to be honest.**

It was a rainy day and Janice wanted to color some pictures in her new animal coloring book. She looked for her crayons, but couldn't find them. She looked for her pencil crayons, but couldn't find them either. Janice went into Jason's room.

On Jason's desk was a new set of magic markers. Janice picked up the red one and drew a line on a pad of paper. It made a bright red mark. "These are just what I need," she thought, and she took the markers into her room.

She colored a purple cow, a pink horse, a blue chicken and a spotted green pig. Then she put the magic markers in a safe place so she wouldn't lose them.

After supper, Jason was doing his homework. He reached for his magic markers to color a map. They weren't there. "Did you see my markers?" he asked his mom and dad.

They both said, "No."

Jason went into Janice's room. "Did you take my magic markers?"

For a moment she was going to say she hadn't taken them. Then she remembered that when she had used her father's spray gun without asking, he had been disappointed that she lied about it. Janice knew it was important to tell the truth. Jason always did.

"I just borrowed them to do some coloring," admitted Janice. "I was going to give them right back, but I forgot." She went to her safe hiding place and pulled them out. "Sorry I didn't ask you."

"That's okay." Jason looked relieved. "But next time, ask me first if you want to borrow something."

---

Sometimes younger brothers and sisters may think it is easier to lie than to tell the truth when they have done something wrong. You can help them by being honest yourself and being understanding about their minor mistakes.

**When you are honest, people trust you.**

Eva, Bobby and Paul were playing in front of Mr. Corban's house. The front door opened and Mr. Corban appeared in his dressing gown.

"I need someone to go to the corner store and buy me bread, milk and orange juice," said Mr. Corban. "I'm not feeling very well today."

"I'll go!" said Paul and Bobby.

"I'll go," offered Eva.

Mr. Corban looked carefully at each of them. "I'm sure you're all honest and can be trusted, but Bobby is the one I know the best. We play checkers every week and he's never let me down. So I hope the rest of you won't be hurt if I pick Bobby to go to the store for me."

Bobby's face shone. He felt proud that Mr. Corban had chosen him. "I'd love to go to the store for you," said Bobby.

Mr. Corban handed Bobby the money and his list of things to buy. "Here's a dollar to spend on yourself. And don't forget to count your change."

"Don't worry," Bobby reassured him. "Arithmetic is my best subject. I'll be back in a flash."

"I wish Mr. Corban had chosen me," Paul complained to Eva after Bobby had left. "I'd sure like a dollar to spend."

"Well, Paul," Eva said gently. "You know you don't have the greatest reputation."

Paul blushed. "I'm working on it."

Before they knew it, Bobby was back with the groceries for Mr. Corban, the correct change and some candy to share with his friends.

---

If you show that you are honest and reliable, people will have confidence in you.

**Honest people return things that don't belong to them.**

Cameron, Ryan and Paul were walking through the park one afternoon, talking about things they wanted.

"I want more money," sighed Cameron. "My allowance never lasts very long."

"I want more fun," said Paul.

"And I want to stay up later at night," added Ryan. They all agreed with that.

Cameron kicked a newspaper in the path and felt something hard. "What was that?" He bent and picked up something brown. "It's a wallet!" he exclaimed, opening it up. "And it's got lots of money in it."

"Well, it's not your money," Paul pointed out. "It belongs to someone else."

"I know, I know. But I can dream, can't I?" said Cameron.

"Let's see if there's a name and address card in it," suggested Ryan.

There was. "Mr. J. Farley," read Cameron. "And here's his phone number."

They went back to Paul's house and phoned Mr. Farley, who was very happy to hear they had found his wallet. "I'll be over right away," he said. They sat on the front steps to wait.

"Look!" exclaimed Ryan as a car drove up. It had a big poster on the side that said: FARLEY'S FALL FAIR, fun for all! "Do you think that's our Mr. Farley?"

"I'm the man who lost the wallet," said Mr. Farley, getting out of the car.

"And I'm the one who found it," explained Cameron.

"Thank you so much," said Mr. Farley, as Cameron gave him back his wallet. "You don't know what this means to me—my credit cards, driver's licence. I thought I'd lost them all."

"And your money," added Cameron.

"Yes, my money," agreed Mr. Farley. "Which reminds me—I want to do something for all of you for finding and returning my wallet."

Mr. Farley pulled three cards out of his pocket and quickly wrote on them. Then he gave each child a card. "Have fun," he said, and drove away.

That night, Paul's parents took Paul, Cameron and Ryan to Farley's Fall Fair. Mr. Farley's cards gave them free admission. But the best part was what was written at the bottom of each card. "Free rides to the bearer of this card, courtesy of J. Farley."

"Roller coaster, here we come!" shouted Paul as they entered the fairground.

By the end of the evening, the boys were tired from all the wild rides and were on the merry-go-round. "This is my favorite ride," said Ryan.

"Mine too," agreed someone on the horse behind him. Ryan looked around and there was Mr. Farley.

"Oh, thank you for your wonderful reward," said Paul.

"Thank you," smiled Mr. Farley.

---

If you are honest, people will trust you and believe in you. Here are some ways you can show honesty:
- Tell the truth.
- Admit when you have done something wrong.
- Do the best you can without cheating.
- Try to be truthful without hurting people's feelings.